MOOMINVALLEY
The Activity Book

Inspired by the works of
TOVE JANSSON

MACMILLAN CHILDREN'S BOOKS

Welcome to Moominvalley

Everything in this activity book has been
inspired by the magical world of Moominvalley
as portrayed in the Moominvalley animation,
where flower beds are edged with shells and sailing
boats are created from tree bark. Like the Moomin
family, their creator Tove Jansson was always inspired
by nature, as are many of the activities in this book.

Some activities are straightforward, some will help you
to switch off, and some will encourage you to think in
a different way. All the activities in this easy-to-use
handbook will inspire creativity that knows no bounds
and encourage you to always see the beauty in the
world around you – just as the Moomins do.

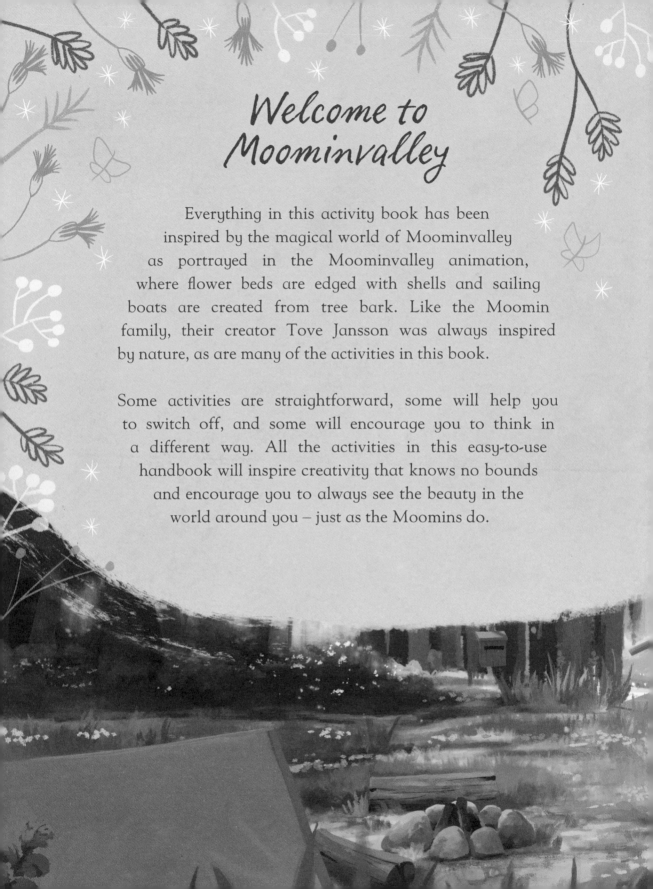

At the end of the book you will find a sheet full of Moomin stickers. You could use these to adorn the pages of the book (some spreads will suggest adding them), but there are plenty of extra stickers that you can use however you want.

A blooming Moominvalley

*'Maybe you shouldn't pick too many of those,
they might be rare . . .'*
Moomintroll, Hattifattener Island

In spring, Moominvalley is filled with the scent of fresh flowers, much to the delight of Snorkmaiden, who loves all things pretty-looking.

*Fill these vases
with flowers.*

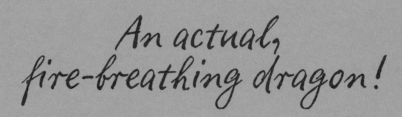

An actual, fire-breathing dragon!

Once, when fishing for wobbly-bugs in the stream, Moomintroll caught a fire-breathing dragon instead. It was quite a find but, as he soon found out, you can take the beast out of the wild, but not the wild out of the beast.

If you could have any pet
(wild or tame), what would it be?
Draw it, or write about it, here.

What would
you call it?

Woodland creatures

Moominvalley is home to many little creatures, who emerge from their cosy winter homes as the snow starts to melt.

Colour in these friendly inhabitants of Moominvalley.

Wonderful water-lilies

'Perfect. Everything is just perfect.'
Moomintroll, Moominsummer Madness

When spring arrives, the stream at the bottom of the slope is in full flow, and his best friend Snufkin is back in Moominvalley, Moomintroll is as happy as a Moomin can be.

Cover the page in water-lilies. *

*You could use your
stickers here too.

Mischievous Little My

'Little My is my name, not my personality.'
Little My, Little My Moves In

As she says, Little My's personality is anything but little. She's afraid of nothing; she says exactly what she thinks and doesn't worry too much about who hears it. Little My wears a flame-red dress which goes with her red hair (and her fiery nature). You definitely don't want to get on the wrong side of her.

13
18
20
17
21
16
22
15
14
24
25
13
23
26
12
27
11
28
10
29
9 8
30
7
6
31
5
32
4
33
34
35
3
36
37
38
2
39

40

1
70
41
69
67 55 54
43 42
68
44
66 56
45 47
65 57
46
63 64 59 51 48
53
62 58 52 50 49
60
61

The marvellous Moominhouse

Nestled amongst the woodlands of Moominvalley sits the Moominhouse. It's tall and bright blue with a red-tiled roof, so it's not hard to spot.

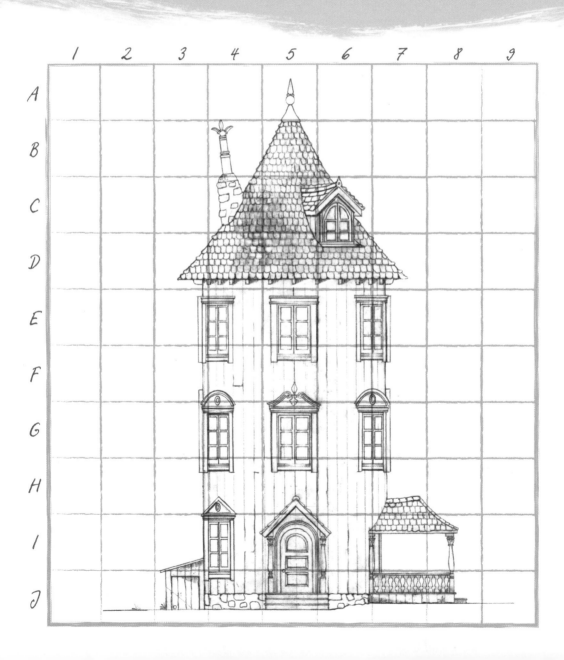

Use the grid to draw
your own perfect replica
of the Moominhouse,
then colour it in.

Is anyone out on the verandah?

	1	2	3	4	5	6	7	8	9
A									
B									
C									
D									
E									
F									
G									
H									
I									
J									

Spring – just like last year

'Spring, finally here again. Just like last year.'
Snorkmaiden, Snufkin and the Park Keeper

In the spring, Moominvalley comes to life after the quiet of winter, which the Moomins (usually!) spend asleep. Plants start to grow, buds burst open and the whole valley shakes off its blanket of snow. But most importantly, (for Moomintroll at least) Snufkin returns to the Moominhouse.

Moominvalley melodies

Snufkin's Spring Tune is legendary throughout Moominvalley. Even the birds like to join in as his melody flows through the woods.

Fill the air with musical notes. You could create them using little fingerprints.

One of the flowers in this display is slightly different from all the others. Can you find it?

The open ocean

What creatures live in the Moominvalley ocean?
(Other than the Mameluke, of course.)
Draw some in.

The mighty Mameluke is
infamous for being the biggest
fish to ever swim the seven seas. *

*The Mameluke may, or may not, be real.

'Every now and again,
I need my space.'

Snufkin, Snufkin and the Park Keeper

Walking alone and liking it

'Now then, about this spring tune . . . One part expectation,
two parts spring sadness, and for the rest, just the great
delight of walking alone and liking it.'
Snufkin, The Spring Tune

Snufkin finds great solace in being alone in the woods
and forests of Moominvalley, listening, looking and
thinking. His spring tune is inspired by the sights,
sounds and feelings he experiences on his walks.

Why don't you go for a stroll,
and try to pay attention to
*the little things you see?**

Where did you walk?

What was the
weather like?

Write down (or maybe draw)
all the things you discovered:

What noises
did you hear?

*It doesn't matter if you live in a
Moominvalley-like forest, a town,
or a big city – there will be things
to notice wherever you are.

Life's simple pleasures

The inhabitants of Moominvalley take great joy in the simple things in life.

Moomintroll likes being in his special place by the pond, where he often goes to think.

Moominpappa loves writing his memoirs, then reading them aloud to his family (and anyone else who will listen).

Snufkin just loves being free to come and go as he pleases.

What simple things in life do you enjoy? Write or draw them here. *

* or you could stick in a photo of you doing something you love.

Snufkin's song

Not much gets Snufkin worked up – he's usually fairly quiet, watching and listening to what's going on around him. He did get cross when the Hemulen Park Keeper locked everyone out of the park, though.

What is Snufkin singing (or shouting) about? Write it in the speech bubble.

How are you feeling?

Nobody can be happy all the time – and the Moomins are no exception. Sometimes sad or unexpected things happen (like when the valley flooded and the Moomin family had to leave their home for somewhere a bit drier). But wonderful things happen too, like when Ninny became visible again, and when Snufkin comes back to the Moominhouse in the spring. Nothing makes Moomintroll happier than that.

Have a look at these creatures' faces and write down how you think they are feeling below.

....

....

....

Excited

Silly

Nervous

Then, for these words, try to draw the emotion above.

About time

The Moomin family have a very handy clock which shows which season they are in. Although it doesn't prevent visitors (like the Mymble and her children) from turning up at unexpected times of year.

Design your own clock face. Instead of adding seasons, why not draw or write on it what you most love spending your time doing.

Do you spend hours exploring like Snufkin, tidying like Mrs. Fillyjonk, or reading and writing, as Moominpappa is often found doing?

A perfectly-proportioned Moomin

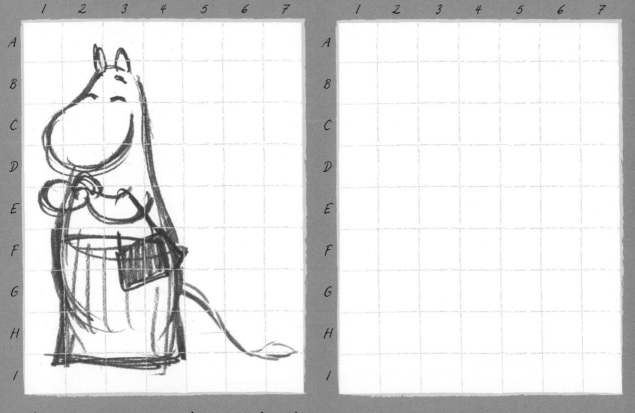

	1	2	3	4	5	6	7			1	2	3	4	5	6	7
A									A							
B									B							
C									C							
D									D							
E									E							
F									F							
G									G							
H									H							
I									I							

Moominmamma is rarely seen without her handbag and her red-and-white-striped apron.

Use the grids to draw Moominmamma and Moominpappa.
By copying one square of the grid at a time, you will be
able to create a perfectly-proportioned Moomin!

And the same goes for Moominpappa
and his smart black hat.

Fingerprint bees

Cover these pages in fingerprint bees. You'll just need some yellow paint and a black pen for the stripes, eyes and wings.

Wait for the paint to dry before you add the black details!

What's in the jar?

Moomintroll often goes fishing in the stream. Once, and very unexpectedly, he caught a dragon. *

Draw some creatures in these jars.

*The dragon did NOT like being stuck in a jar, probably because Moomintroll forgot to give it some airholes.

'There are lots of things
one can't understand.
But why should things stay
exactly as we are used to?'

Moominmamma, Moominsummer Madness

Invisible creatures

When the Moomins encounter the Invisible Child (or Ninny as it turns out she is called) they try to make her feel as welcome as possible. Moominmamma gives her a bell to wear so that she can be heard, even if she can't yet be seen.

What do you think
these invisible creatures
might look like?
Draw their bodies!

*It turns out that the best cure for
invisibility is listening. It stops people
being see-through in no time!

What has scared Sniff?

Sniff is a very well-meaning but often slightly troublesome member of the extended Moomin family. He's sort of like an annoying younger brother to Moomintroll. He loves the *idea* of adventures, especially the thought of being rewarded for doing something heroic, but in reality he doesn't particularly like them and gets scared very easily. *

What has scared
Sniff this time?

* Though he did save Moominmamma and Moominpappa from the
Groke once, so sometimes he shows surprising resourcefulness!

Cloud games

When Moomintroll dropped eggshells into the Hobgoblin's magic hat, they became fluffy clouds to zoom about on.

Draw some more fluffy clouds and colour them in.

*What colour are your clouds?

Can you find any cloud-like textures to make your clouds? How about dipping cotton wool in paint? Or dipping a twig in ink and making a cloud out of squiggles?

All small beasts should have bows in their tails

At least, that's the case according to the well-known Moominvalley song of that name. (It's one of Little My's favourites.)

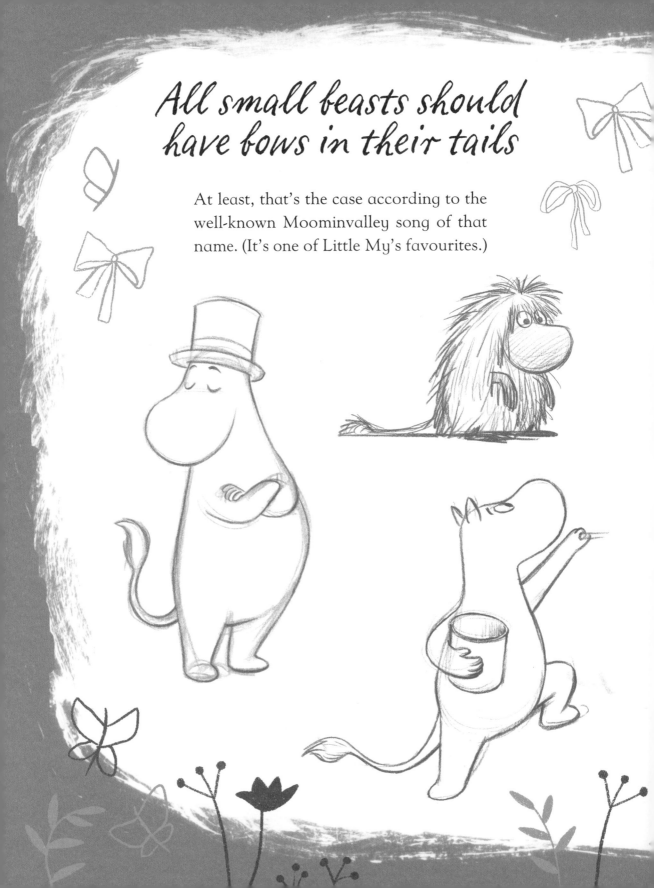

Give these familiar Moominvalley inhabitants bows in their tails. The more extravagant, the better!

*You could use your stickers here, too.

Emma the Stage Rat

*'My name is Emma, and I was
but a lowly stage hand . . .'*
Emma the Stage Rat, Moominsummer Madness

Emma the Stage Rat lives, as her name suggests, on the stage,
where she feels most at home. She certainly has a flair for the
dramatic, and enjoys teaching the Moomins about theatre
or, as she calls it: 'the temple of dreams'. She even helped the
Moomin family (well, mainly Moominpappa, who has a flair
for the dramatic too), put on a play themselves.

Join the dots to create
Emma the Stage Rat
then colour her in.

Neat and tidy

*'Well, I don't know what to say,
Mrs Fillyjonk. It's quite a vision.'*
Moominmamma, Moominmamma's Maid

Fillyjonks have very high standards of organisation and are very neat and tidy, at *all* times. They can't bear the thought of mess or anything being out of place.

Continue this very precise pattern all over the opposite page to please your inner fillyjonk!*

*The Moomins themselves take a much more relaxed approach to tidiness. If you're more moomin than fillyjonk, don't feel you have to stick to the rules – do whatever you want on this page!

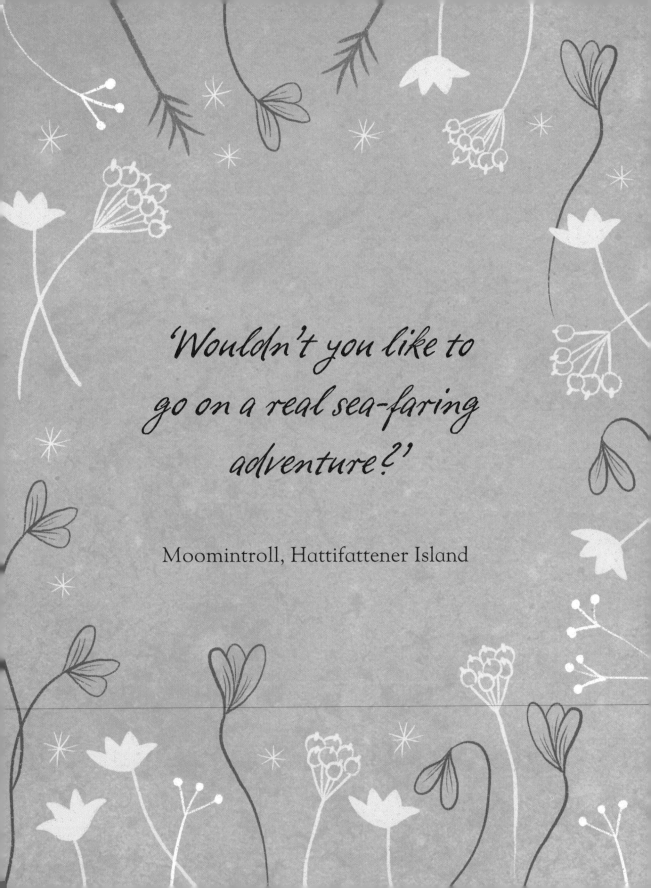

'Wouldn't you like to
go on a real sea-faring
adventure?'

Moomintroll, Hattifattener Island

Secret islands

The Moomins sometimes discover new islands in the sea around Moominvalley. Exploring uncharted territory is always exciting – and often surprising!

Draw your own
secret island.

Does it have a lighthouse? Rock pools?
A beach house? Is there anyone — or
anything — living on the island?

The first bark boat of the summer

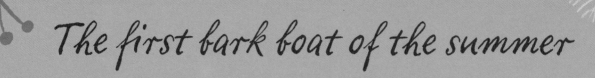

*'One big sail on the main mast, one on the mizzen,
and a hatch on the deck, just in case of hurricanes.'*
Moominmamma, Moominsummer Madness

Each year, at the start of summer,
Moominmamma makes a bark boat
for Moomintroll.

Design your own
boat below.

Is it a sailing boat, a rowboat,
or maybe a Viking ship?

One of the flowers in this display is slightly different from all the others.
Can you find it?

Ebb and flow

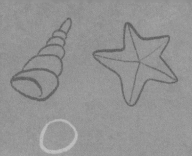

When they're not out sailing the open sea, the Moomins love to walk along the shore, seeing what the tide has thrown up. Moomintroll is always on the look out for a 'rarey object' – a special find.

Next time you are by the sea or a river, sit quietly on the shore. What do you notice? Write or draw it here.

What can you hear? Is the water crashing against rocks, or lapping on sand?

Have you ever found any
'rarey objects' on a beach?
Write a list of your found
treasures here:

Hundreds of hattifatteners

Hattifatteners are strange, silent beings. They travel in groups and look a bit like small white mushroom stalks, with pale eyes and frilly hands on either side.

See how many hattifatteners you can squeeze onto this page.

Watch out – hattifatteners are especially electric when newly grown!

The catch of a lifetime!

Moominpappa and Moomintroll often head out to sea together to fish the open ocean. But they have been known to exaggerate the stories of their fishing adventures!

Draw the 'catch of a lifetime' at the end of Moominpappa's fishing rod. *

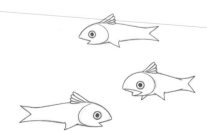

It doesn't have to be a fish!

You should never build a house on sand

Moomintroll found this to be the case when he tried to build himself a new home on the beach that quickly sunk without a trace. He found a sturdy-looking rock and tried again, but the rock turned out to be a turtle, and the house became more of a mobile home, which was quite a wonderful surprise.

Design your own mobile home on the turtle's back.

Where's the first place you would visit?

'It's the wild,
free life for us!'

Moominpappa, Night of the Groke

A memoir worthy of Moominpappa

As Moominpappa often mentions, he has led a very brave and exciting life. He even directed a play about it!

Write about something exciting that has happened to you. *

*If you want to exaggerate to make it more dramatic, that's absolutely fine. Moominpappa does the same thing.

A walk with the woodies

Woodies are furry little creatures, sort of like small children. Snufkin accidentally becomes a father-figure to a group of them when he liberates a park (where the woodies had been living) from a very strict Hemulen Park Keeper. The woodies love Snufkin; he's not sure about them. He's not used to children. He doesn't even know if he likes them . . .

Draw a line of woodies walking across the page. You could use your woodie stickers too.

They often hold the tail of the woodie in front, so nobody gets left behind!

Snufkin

Snufkin is a deep-thinking wanderer, who is rarely seen without his green hat and his harmonica, on which he composes his Spring Tune. He doesn't need, or want, many possessions, and carries everything he owns in his backpack.

Moomintroll admires Snufkin and his independent ways, and every spring eagerly awaits the arrival of his best friend.

Apple juice

There are plenty of apple trees in Moominvalley, and when the time is right, the Moomin family can often be found picking up windfalls to make apple juice.

Draw the treetop and fill it with apples. You could use some of your stickers here too.

Draw the dragon

'By my everlasting tail. It's a dragon!'
Moomintroll, The Last Dragon

When Moomintroll asks Snufkin if he's ever come across a dragon on his wanderings, Snufkin thinks he might mean a salamander, a lizard or a crocodile. Dragons are extinct. Or so Snufkin thinks . . .

Use the grid below to draw the dragon by copying one square of the grid at a time, then colour it in.

Autumn leaves

'Nature! It's so untidy.'
Mrs Fillyjonk, Moominmamma's Maid

Make this page as untidy
as you can by covering it
in autumn leaves.

Red, yellow, orange and brown pencils at the ready!

Giant-footed forest ogres

Footprints can be misleading. What Sniff thinks are the tracks of a giant-footed forest ogre turn out to be the footprints of Snufkin, who was seeing what life is like in someone else's shoes (uncomfortable).

Cover the page with footprints and tracks.

Where do they lead?

A name of one's own

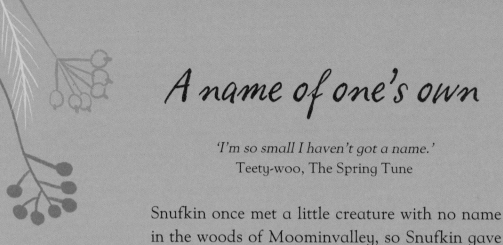

'I'm so small I haven't got a name.'
Teety-woo, The Spring Tune

Snufkin once met a little creature with no name in the woods of Moominvalley, so Snufkin gave him one: Teety-woo. Having a name made a big difference – Teety-woo soon became very busy and felt much more important.

There are lots of creatures living in Moominvalley who would probably love a proper name. Give them one below.

Scaring season

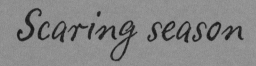

*'When the pumpkin's full and orange, and the woods
are dark and eerie, it's supposed to be my time.
Trouble is, I'm just no good at scaring!'*
The Ghost, Ghost Story

The Ghost wants to be much scarier than he is, which
isn't very scary at all. He wasn't even able to scare
Moomintroll. And that's saying something!

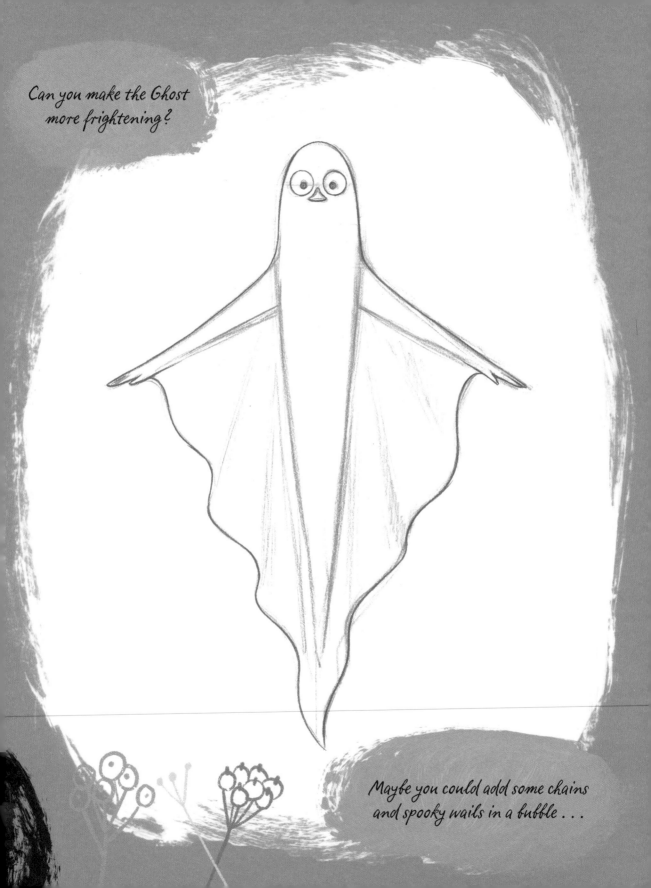

Can you make the Ghost more frightening?

Maybe you could add some chains and spooky wails in a bubble . . .

Falling snow

'If we sleep through the winter we'll miss all the snow.'
Moomintroll, Midwinter Ancestor

Moomins usually hibernate during winter (after a big supper of pine needles), so they're not very familiar with snow. But, one year, Moomintroll wakes up to find a winter wonderland!

Cover these pages with drifting snowflakes.

You could draw them with different coloured pens, paint them, or even make some paper snowflakes and stick them in!